written by **Claire Philip**

Illustrated by **Steven Wood**

At the station

We travel on trains to visit friends and family, go on holiday or get to work. Trains can carry lots of people at once!

Sleeper trains

23.45 PLATFORM 6
EDINBURGH

6

Did you know that some trains have beds on board?

A-D →

CALEDONIAN SLEEPER

Delicious!

Can I help you?

The Caledonian Sleeper travels between London and Scotland, UK. People eat in the restaurant cart.

Below ground

Trains can travel underground! These trains transport people through tunnels, from station to station beneath the city.

Subway, metro, tube – different countries use different names for their underground train systems.

Across the city

Beat the traffic and jump on a train to get across the city!

The Las Vegas Monorail is completely electric, which means it gives out no pollution!

Terrific trams

Shorter and lighter than trains, trams whizz around towns and cities. Most are powered by electric wires that run overhead.

Trams often share roads with cars and buses.

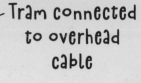
Tram connected to overhead cable

41

41

4027

The first trams were pulled by horses!

Tramway

All kinds of train!

There are many different types of train. Have you seen any of these?

Mining train

I can pull lots of wagons at once!

I burn coal or wood to heat up water and make steam.

Steam train

I have two levels, like a double-decker bus!

Bullet trains

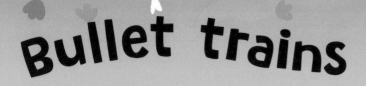

The fastest train system in the world is called the Shinkansen in Japan. Its trains are called bullet trains because they shoot across the country!

Smooth rails help me speed along the track!

Magnet Power!

Is that train floating along the track?
No! It's being pulled up by magnets!
Maglev is short for magnetic levitation.

Maglev trains are super-fast
due to their sleek shape and
because there is very little
friction on the rails.

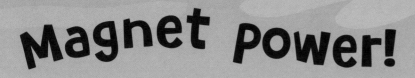

Magnets on the underside of the train
create a force that either pushes or pulls
against magnets on the track.

Freight trains

Powerful freight trains pull carriages filled with heavy goods, from grain to cars! Some pull hundreds of carriages at a time.

This Union Pacific train is carrying cargo across the United States.

Honk!

4837

Freight trains travel hundreds of kilometres without stopping.

Here are some of the different kinds of freight carriage.

Gondola

I'm carrying building materials.

Cistern

I transport liquids or gases!

Boxcar

Today I'm transporting food!

Platform

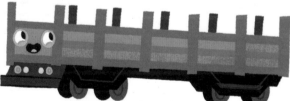

Hopper

I carry things like cement or grains.

Amazing journeys

Trains travel through all kinds of beautiful landscapes.

The Indonesian train Argo Parahyangan passes over steep valleys and a tall, narrow bridge.

Passengers onboard the Trans-Siberian Express pass through snowy Russia, Mongolia and China.

The Ghan takes passengers on a train adventure right across the rocky Australian desert.

It takes eight hours to travel the beautiful Glacier Express route through the Swiss Alps.

Amazing views!

The US Coast Starlight passes stunning scenery, from mountain peaks to beaches and forests!

Famous trains

Climb aboard these famous trains and explore different countries!

Royal Scotsman, the Scottish Highlands

Explore the mountains and glens with me!

Deccan Queen, India

I'm off to Mumbai!

Under the sea

Eurostar trains travel under the sea! They speed through a tunnel beneath the English Channel, between France and the UK.

As the train races through the tunnel, it is 75 metres below the ocean's surface.